John McWilliams

For my children and grandchildren
John McWilliams

To Rossco and Romy, my little drawing companion
Rose Forshall

First published 2023 by Mabecron Books

Mabecron Books Ltd
Briston Orchard, St Mellion, Saltash
Cornwall P12 6RQ United Kingdom

Printed in Italy

ISBN 978-1-7398613-1-5

Mabecron Books

The Good SHIP TRUE LOVE

WORDS BY
John McWilliams

PICTURES BY
Rose Forshall

There was once a street in Penzance, it was called Camberwell Street. The people who lived there hardly had any money, but they always looked out for each other.

An old sailor man called Mr Ellis was living in one of the small, terraced houses. His wife had died, and his grown-up sons had all gone to work in the coal mines of Wales.

One day, as he was cooking a mackerel for tea, he had an extraordinary idea.
'I'd really love to have a boat like the boats when I was a lad. I'd be able to earn my living as a fisherman again.'
'But I don't have any money to buy a boat,' he quickly realised.
'I'll build one!' he decided. 'In my back yard. I'll just do my best to build it there then.'

But Mr Ellis had never built a boat before. He came from Brixham, a famous fishing town in Devon where the trawlers, with their lovely red sails, fished all around the coastline of England and Wales.

He liked to watch the boats whenever he could, and to recall his memories from days gone by. He remembered the local women making the fishermen's nets and how they used a special net needle to mend the holes. When the children came home from school they helped by filling the needles with twine. That was an important job and had to be done before they were allowed out to play!

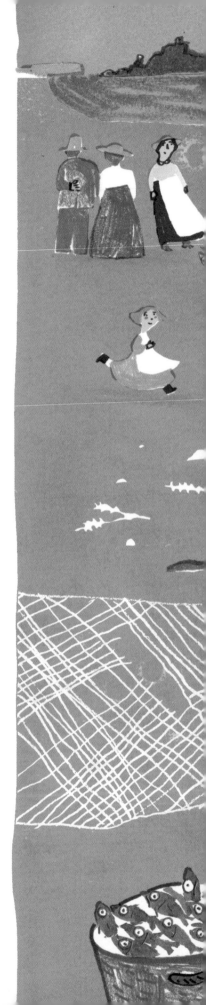

To build his boat, Mr Ellis knew he would need plenty of wood, so he found some builders working on a nearby house:
'Please Mister, can I have those old floorboards?'
'That's alright Mr Ellis, you can have them, my handsome,' replied the friendly builder.
'Thank you. They'll be the very thing for building my boat.'

At his local shop he asked, 'Please Mister can I have those empty orange boxes?'
'Yes you can Mr Ellis. You just help yourself, whatever you have a mind to,'
encouraged the friendly grocer.
'Thank you. They'll be the very thing for building my boat.'

Mr Ellis set to work laying the keel and adding the ribs. The neighbours heard Mr Ellis hammering away and came out to see what was happening.
'Whatever are you doing Mr Ellis?'
'I'm building my boat,' he explained.
'My goodness, so you are!' they all replied in astonishment.

It took a long time to collect enough wood to build the next part of the boat. Mr Ellis worked hard, gathering more and more floorboards and more and more orange boxes.

After the ribs were in place he began to nail on the planks. He hammered them all on one side first and then tipped the boat over to do the other side. He knew they were not quite the same on both sides but hoped it would turn out alright.

In winter he warmed his freezing hands with a cup of cocoa, and when the rain came down, he took his pieces of wood into the kitchen and sawed them into shape there.

The boat grew bigger and BIGGER and soon filled the whole of the back yard. Mr Ellis decided it was time for some drastic action.

Millie and her friends heard a loud tap, tap, tap from behind the wall and came round to find out what was happening.
'Stand back,' he shouted as the lane wall came tumbling down.

'Well Millie, what do you think of her?'
'I truly love your boat Mr Ellis. It is beautiful.'
Mr Ellis smiled, 'Thank you Millie, I think you've given me an idea.'

'My goodness Mr Ellis! That's some brer great boat you've got there. How ever are you going to get it out?' exclaimed his neighbours.

In the Spring, Penzance Harbour was filled
with a whole fleet of drifters, arrived from
Lowestoft for the mackerel season. Each
boat had a crew of up to twelve which
meant there were hundreds of fishermen
going out each evening, and hauling in
their night-time catch.

When the Lowestoft fishermen heard
about Mr Ellis and the boat he built,
they decided to lend a hand.
'Let's get ourselves up there,' they all
agreed, 'and see what we can do to help.'

When the men arrived in Camberwell Street they got to work. They called out, **'Heave Oh! Heave oh!'** and pulled the boat out into the lane.

'Way hey … and Up she goes!' they shouted and lifted the boat up onto its trolley.

With a final **'Heave oh!'** they began to pull her down the narrow lane.

It was a very tight squeeze and the boat soon got stuck.
'Don't you worry about a thing Mr Ellis, we'll sort this out,'
and the Lowestoft fishermen, without any hesitation,
pulled the wall down.

The next day Mr Ellis arrived at Penzance Customs House. 'Please Mister,' he asked the Customs Officer, 'I'd like to register my new boat.'

'Let's measure how **LONG**, how **WIDE**, and how **DEEP** your boat is Mr Ellis.'

'What is the name of your boat Mr Ellis?' he asked.
'*True Love*,' declared Mr Ellis, 'She's called *True Love*,' he said again, recalling Millie's words when she first saw his boat.

Mr Ellis painted **TRUE LOVE • PENZANCE** in big white letters on the stern of his boat. Millie was thrilled when she saw what it was called. For a while they both enjoyed looking up at the name. It was a fine boat they thought.

Then Millie said, 'When I grow up Mr Ellis, I want to build a boat just like you.'

The final task was to make three sails for
True Love – a LARGE mainsail and
two smaller ones to go in front.

Every piece was cut from a large
secondhand sail his friends had found.

Mr Ellis sewed the pieces together and attached a rope around the edge of each sail. He used a large sailmaker's needle and special palm tool for pushing each stitch through the very strong and thick canvas.

Mr Ellis was pleased with his work.
'That will do nicely,' he said to Millie.

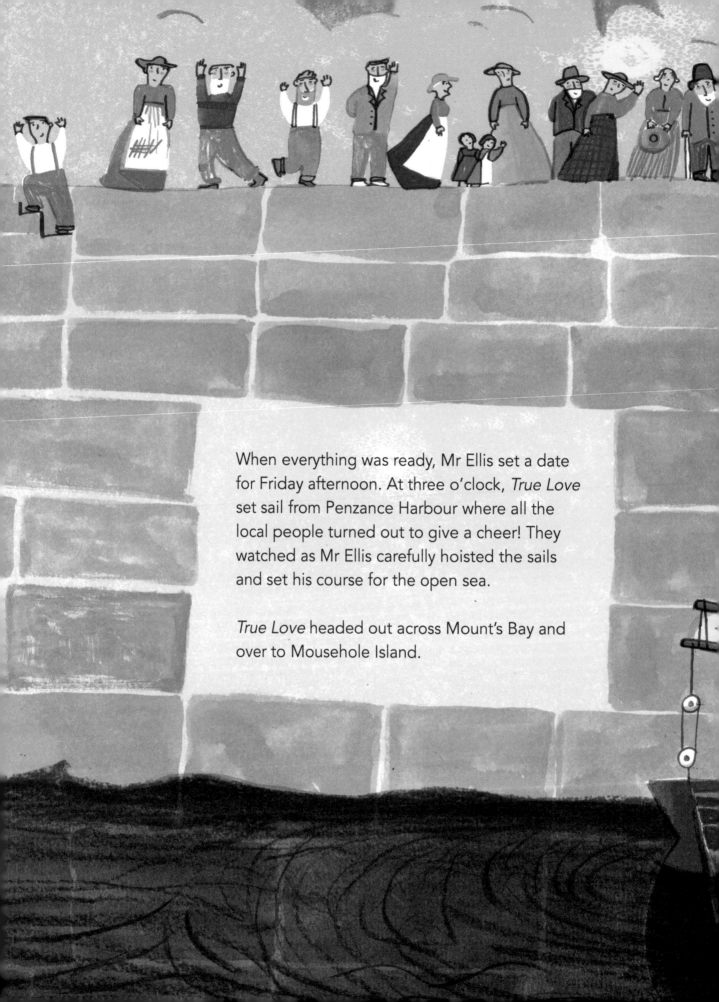

When everything was ready, Mr Ellis set a date
for Friday afternoon. At three o'clock, *True Love*
set sail from Penzance Harbour where all the
local people turned out to give a cheer! They
watched as Mr Ellis carefully hoisted the sails
and set his course for the open sea.

True Love headed out across Mount's Bay and
over to Mousehole Island.

Crowds lined the coast as she sailed back and forth on her first voyage. Many more people came to see her than ever came to see Lord Brassey's famous yacht, the *Sunbeam*, which often anchored in the Bay.

On her second outing *True Love* sailed over to Newlyn where hundreds more people came down the North Pier to catch sight of the now famous boat. They did notice that she leaned over a bit and that she was not quite the same on both sides.

The story of Mr Ellis and *True Love* was in the
local newspaper.

The Cornishman

A curious boat was launched lately at Penzance. It was
the work of an old seafaring man of 70, named Ellis,
who made it out of old pieces of wood, chiefly orange
boxes, in his back yard. The boat was carried down to
the water, and while en route, stuck in a narrow street,
and a wall had to be pulled down to let it pass. It has
been romantically christened True Love, but its name
among the Penzance people is The Ark.

But a boat made of floorboards and orange boxes will not last long,
and it was soon time to put *True Love* ashore at Eastern Green.
Millie and all the children climbed in with Mr Ellis and had their
photograph taken.
'You did it Mr Ellis, you built your boat!' they cheered.

Mr Ellis was quietly proud of his extraordinary achievement, even if he didn't make any money as a fisherman. With some help along the way, he made his dream come true. He *really did* build *True Love* in his own backyard, and she *really did* sail the choppy waters around Mount's Bay for everyone to see.